Help Spider-Man through the maze to meet his team.

START

FINISH

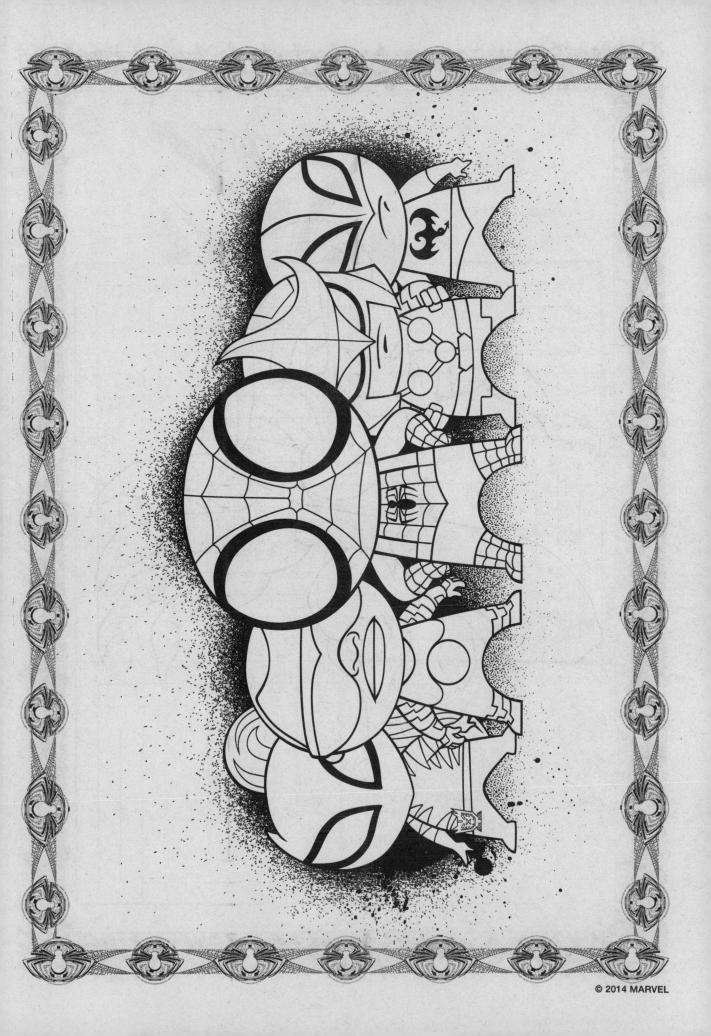

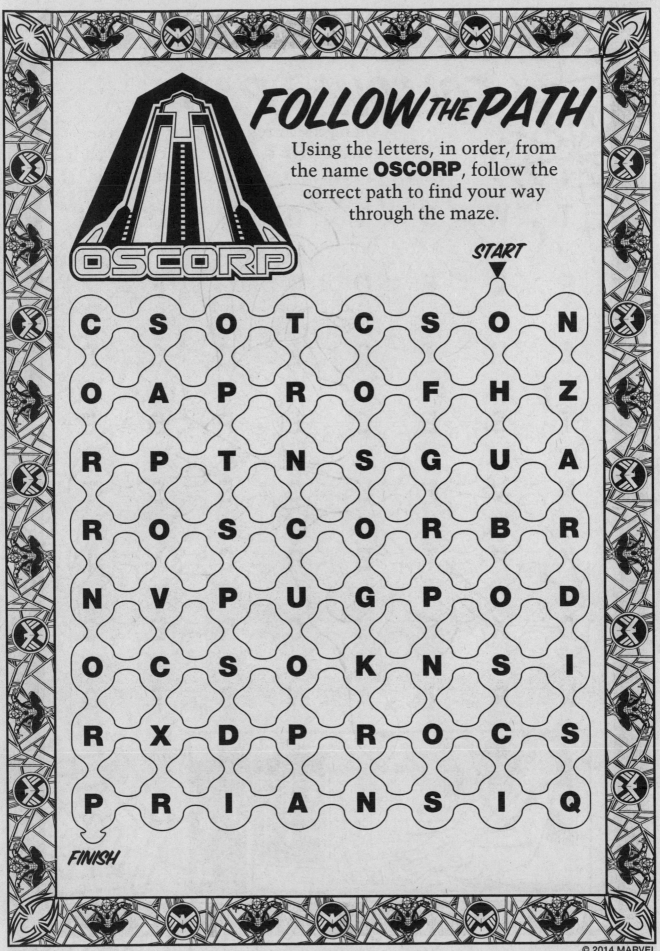

FOLLOW *the* PATH

Using the letters, in order, from the name **OSCORP**, follow the correct path to find your way through the maze.

OSCORP

START

FINISH

FOLLOW THE PATH

START ▼

Using the letters, in order, from the name **SECRET**, follow the correct path to find your way through the maze.

T	W	S	T	G	Y	Q	N
R	C	E	Q	T	S	E	Z
E	R	T	R	E	G	C	R
T	S	E	C	L	P	B	E
N	V	P	U	G	E	S	T
K	P	T	E	R	C	A	I
G	X	S	E	C	R	E	S
N	R	I	A	N	S	T	Q

FINISH

WORD SCRAMBLE

Using the words from the list, unscramble the letters to correctly spell the names and words.

INCK URFY_____

ETHWIRIETG_____

PWROEANM_____

NROI TFIS_____

OANV_____

© 2014 MARVEL

Match each of Peter Parker's friends
to his or her Super Hero identity.

DANNY RAND   AVA AYALA   LUKE CAGE   SAM ALEXANDER

NOVA   POWER MAN   WHITE TIGER   IRON FIST

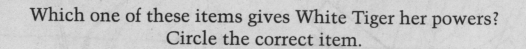

Which one of these items gives White Tiger her powers?
Circle the correct item.

Match each Super Hero to his or her name.

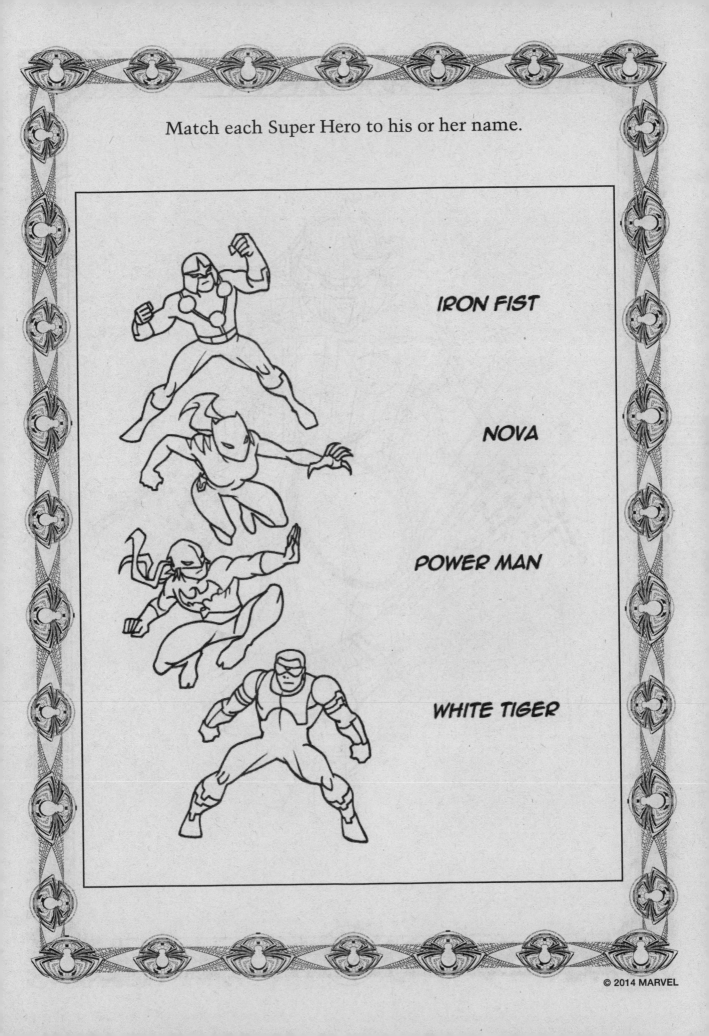

IRON FIST

NOVA

POWER MAN

WHITE TIGER

Which staircase should Spider-Man use to enter Dr. Doom's castle?

A B C

© 20

Circle the drawing of the superpower that Spider-Man DOESN'T have.

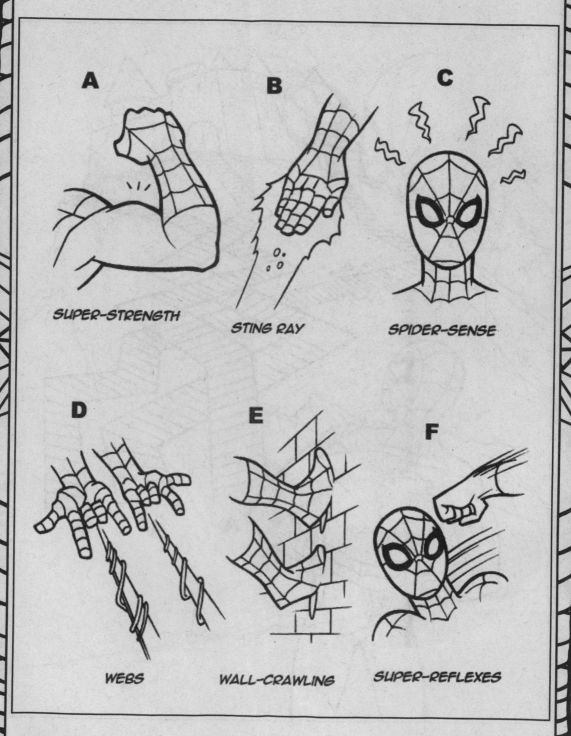

A
SUPER-STRENGTH

B
STING RAY

C
SPIDER-SENSE

D
WEBS

E
WALL-CRAWLING

F
SUPER-REFLEXES

ANSWER: Power B, Sting Ray

Which door did Dr. Doom take?
Follow the tangled lines to find out!

Friend or Foe? Circle the three friends of Spider-Man.

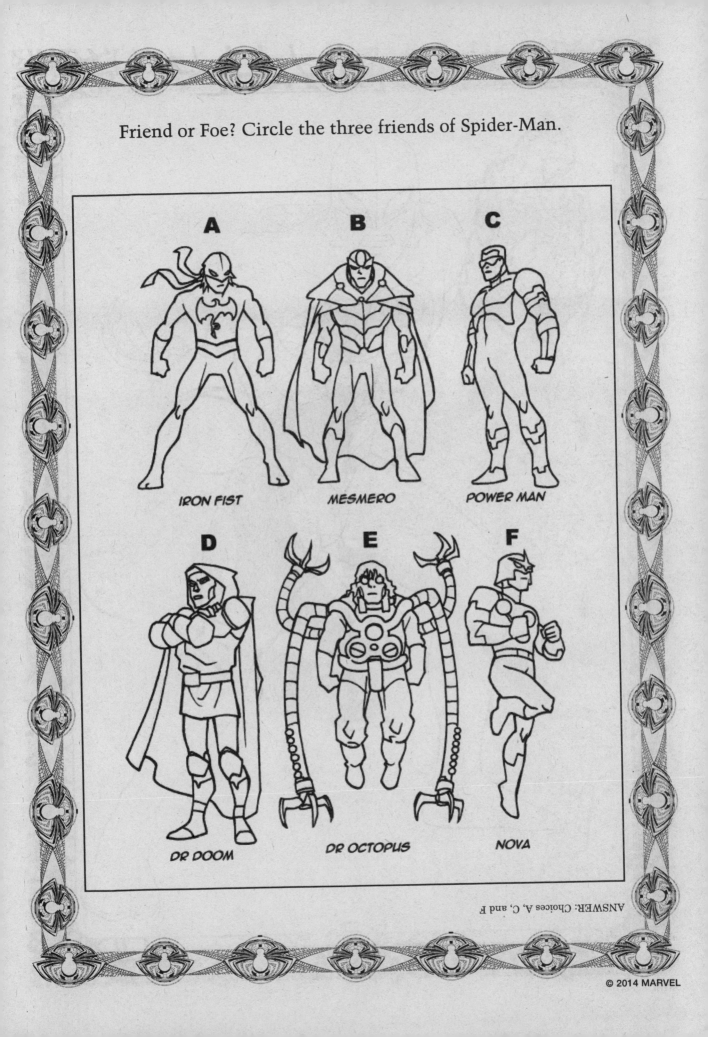

A
IRON FIST

B
MESMERO

C
POWER MAN

D
DR DOOM

E
DR OCTOPUS

F
NOVA

Real or Robot?
Circle the drawing that matches the real Dr. Doom exactly.

Help Peter Parker choose the right Spider-Man costume.

A

B

C

D

Help Spider-Man navigate the hedge maze
to get back inside Dr. Doom's castle.

Which one of these people from Peter's life has a secret identity as a super villain?

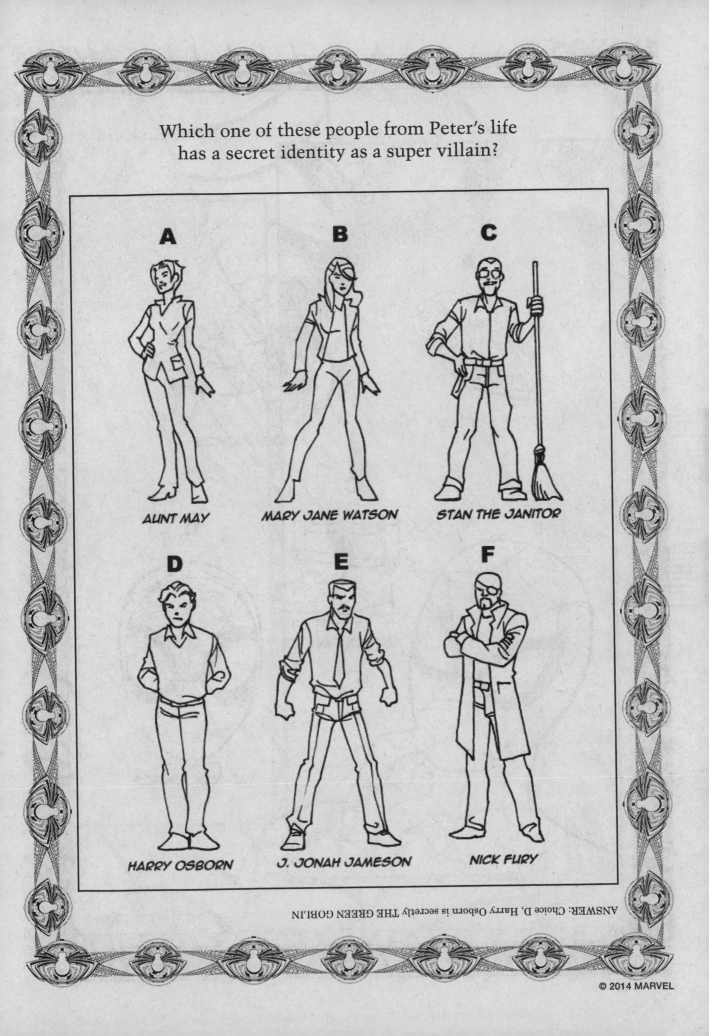

A

AUNT MAY

B

MARY JANE WATSON

C

STAN THE JANITOR

D

HARRY OSBORN

E

J. JONAH JAMESON

F

NICK FURY

ANSWER: Choice D, Harry Osborn is secretly THE GREEN GOBLIN

Which one of these gadgets does Spider-Man NOT have?

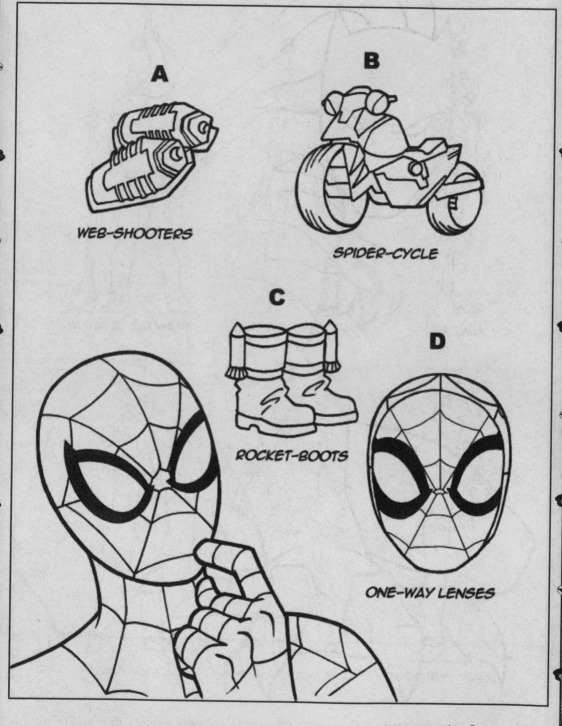

A

WEB-SHOOTERS

B

SPIDER-CYCLE

C

ROCKET-BOOTS

D

ONE-WAY LENSES

ANSWER: Gadget C, Rocket Boots

© 2014 MARVEL

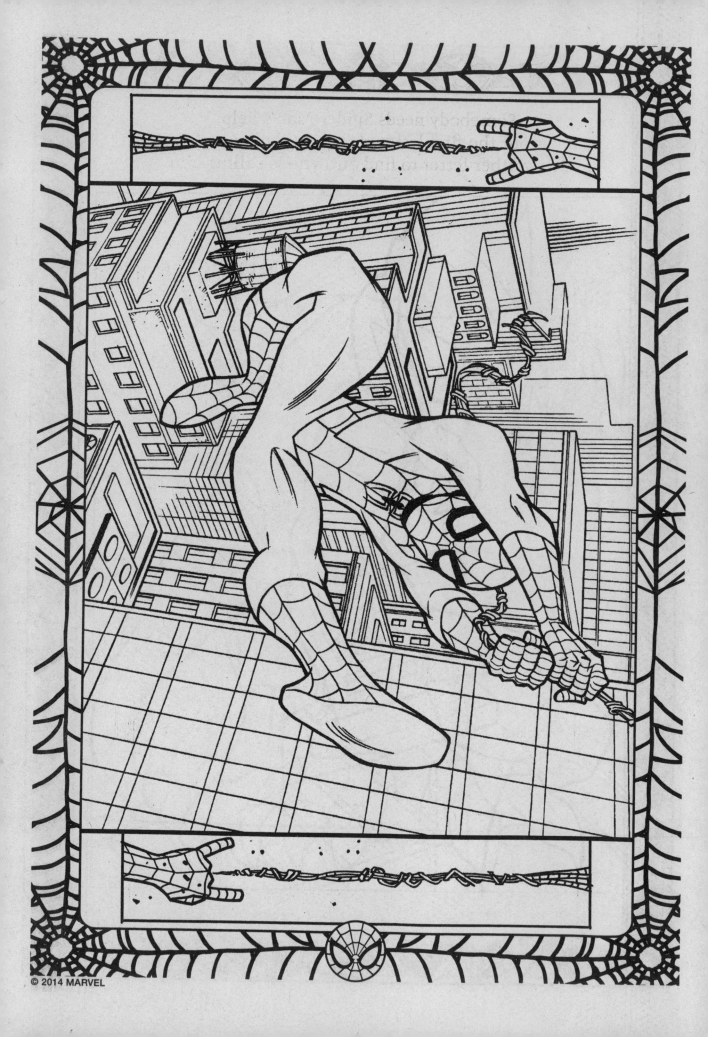

Somebody needs Spider-Man's help!
Cross out the first letter of the clue below and then
every other letter to find out who is calling him.

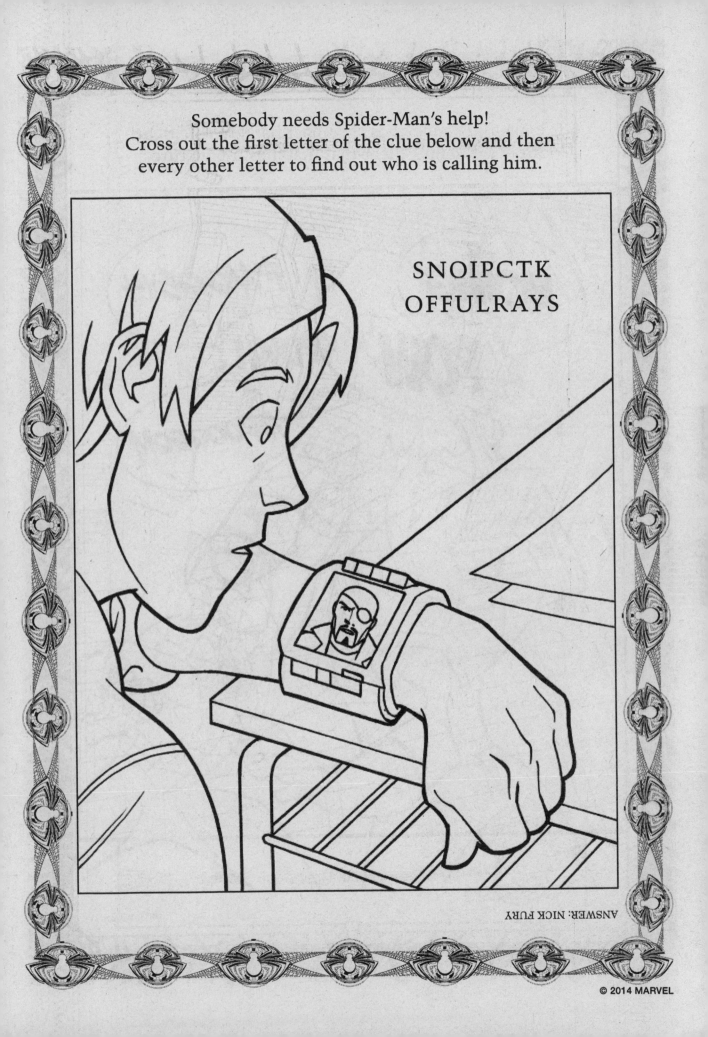

SNOIPCTK
OFFULRAYS

It looks like Spidey has the upper hand in this fight!
Circle the sound effect that matches the picture.

Spider-Man needs to change into his secret identity, Peter Parker. Can you help him find his hidden clothes on the rooftop?

ANSWER: His clothes are in a web on the side of the shed.

Can you spot Spider-Man hiding in the woods?

ANSWER: Spider-man is in the top of a tree, haning down, on the top right of the picture.

FILL-INS
Fill in the word ballons to finish the story!

Help Spider-Man find the safest tree branch to hang onto.
Circle the branch he should grab.

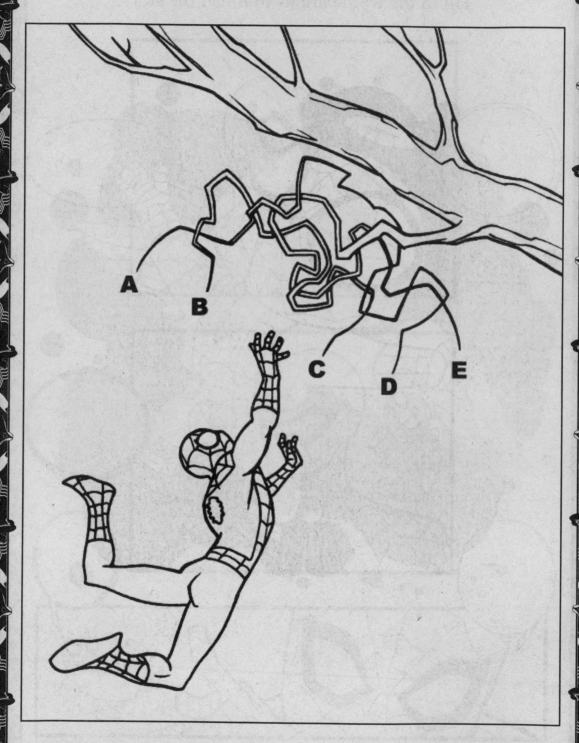

Spider-Man is heading to Dr. Doom's castle in Latveria.
Which jet should he take to get there?

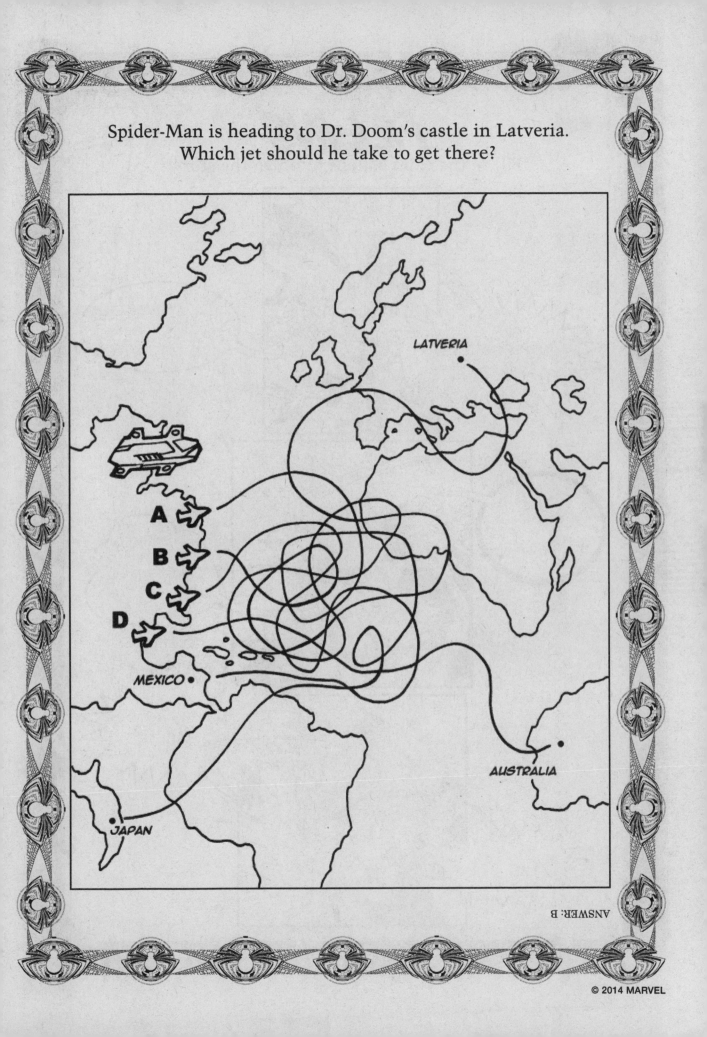

FILL-INS

Fill in the word ballons to finish the story!

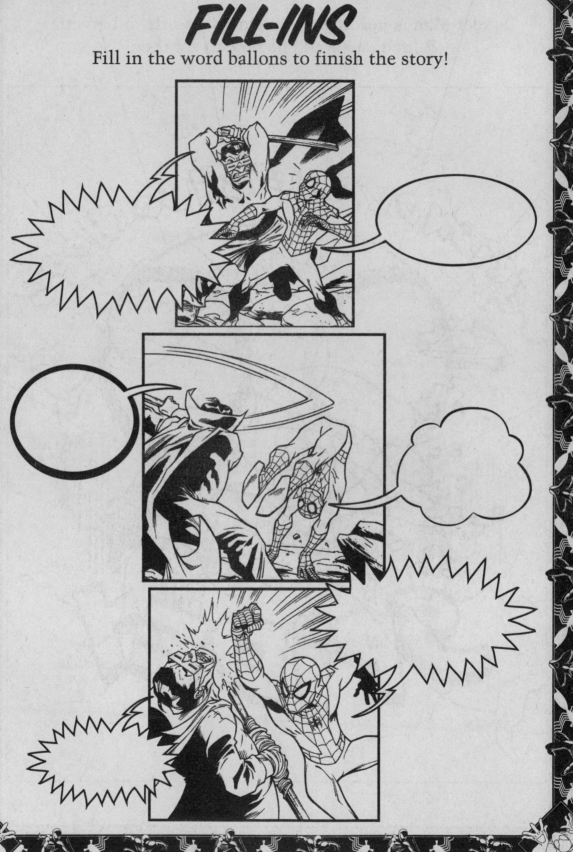

Dr. Doom is gone, but Spidey's spider-sense is telling him danger is nearby. Find the reason why and circle it.

ANSWER: There is a bomb in the third cell.

Help Peter get to class undetected.
Which hallway should he take to avoid being seen?

Peter's watch is ringing. Connect the dots
to make his invisible communicator appear!

Which web will lead Spider-Man inside the S.H.I.E.L.D. Helicarrier?

A B C D

Which shadow matches Spider-Man exactly?

Part of the story is missing! Fill in the missing comic panel.

Robot Nick Fury has hacked into S.H.I.E.L.D.'s defense systems. Complete the maze and help Spider-Man navigate his way through the laser field.

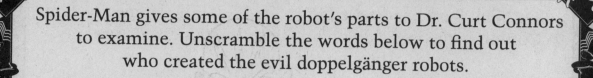

Spider-Man gives some of the robot's parts to Dr. Curt Connors to examine. Unscramble the words below to find out who created the evil doppelgänger robots.

TROCDO OMOD!

Spidey word search! Can you find these words in the puzzle below? Look up, down, backward, forward, and diagonally.

Dr. Octopus	Fury	Mary Jane	Nova	Osborn
SHIELD	Spider-Man	Ultimate	Venom	Webs

```
E  M  A  R  Y  J  A  N  E  T
T  S  H  I  E  L  D  N  T  S
A  N  R  O  B  S  O  C  P  U
M  O  D  R  S  V  W  A  B  P
I  U  L  B  A  H  C  O  P  O
T  J  E  L  M  K  I  B  L  T
L  W  H  F  O  V  T  E  T  C
U  T  B  U  N  E  E  R  L  O
N  A  M  R  E  D  I  P  S  R
S  P  R  Y  V  U  J  A  N  D
```

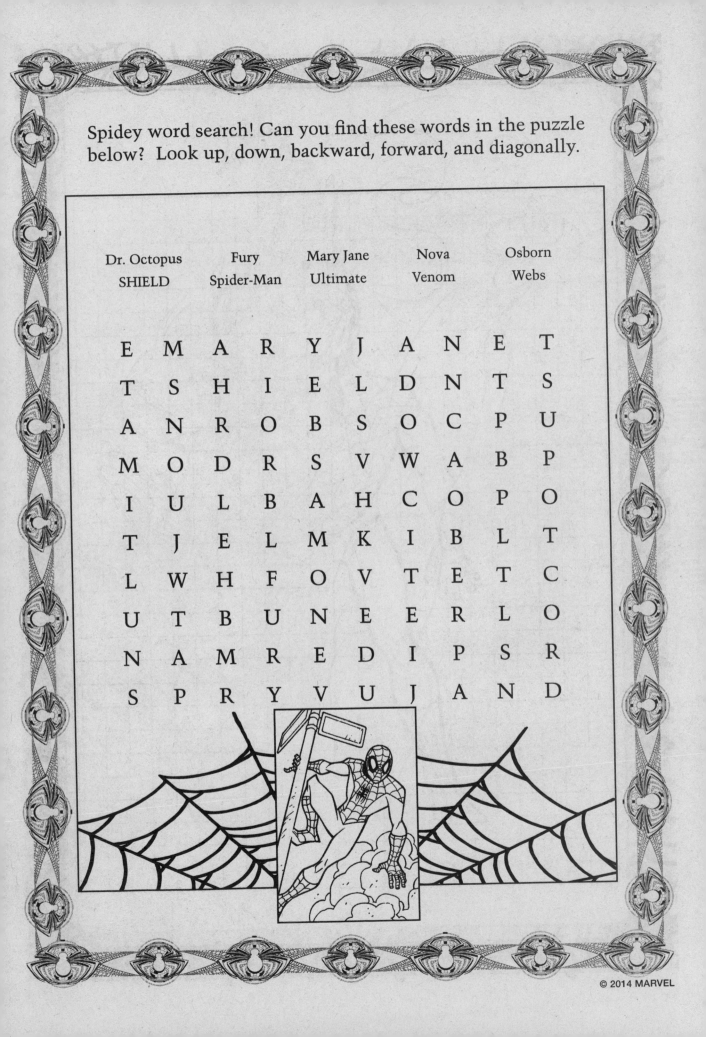

Draw the other half of Spider-Man!

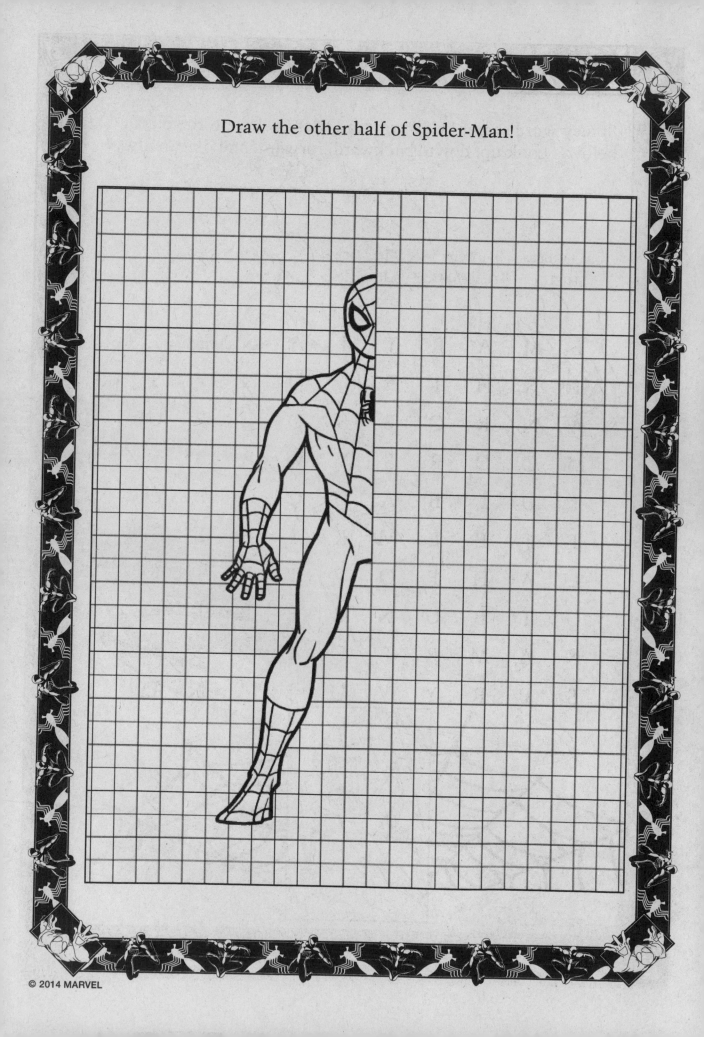

TRANSFER

Using the paths, transfer the letters into
the boxes to unscramble the word.

T I I A Y G L

MATCHING

Draw lines to connect EACH image and
ITS matching SILHOUETTE.

SECRET MESSAGE

Cross out the word **SPIDERMAN** every time you see it in the box. When you reach a letter that does not belong, write it in the circles below to reveal the secret message.

SPIDERMANSPIDERMAN
SPIDERMANASPIDERMAN
GSPIDERMANRSPIDERMAN
SPIDERMANESPIDERMAN
SPIDERMANSPIDERMANA
SPIDERMANTSPIDERMAN
ESPIDERMANRSPIDERMAN
SPIDERMANGSPIDERMAN
SPIDERMANOSPIDERMANO
SPIDERMANDSPIDERMAN

MISSING PIECE

Find the missing piece of the image and finish the drawing of Venom!

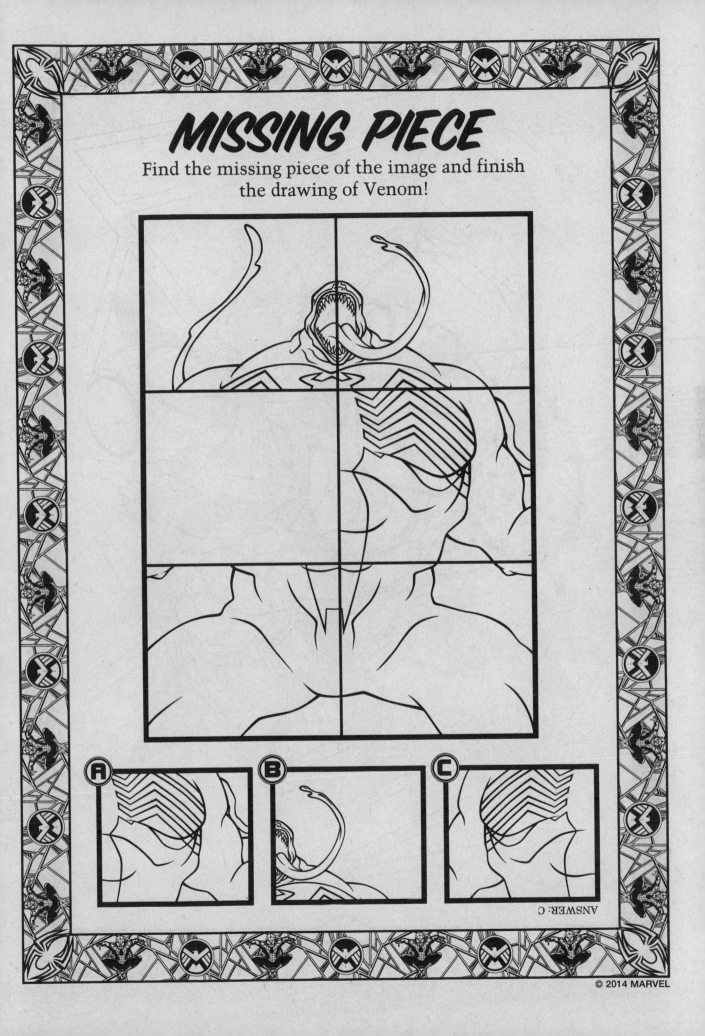

How many words can you spell using the letters in TASKMASTER?

EXAMPLE:

MASK

Spider-Man leaps from the jet!
Connect the dots to see how he plans to land safely in Latveria.

Circle the villain who has the power to create tornadoes.

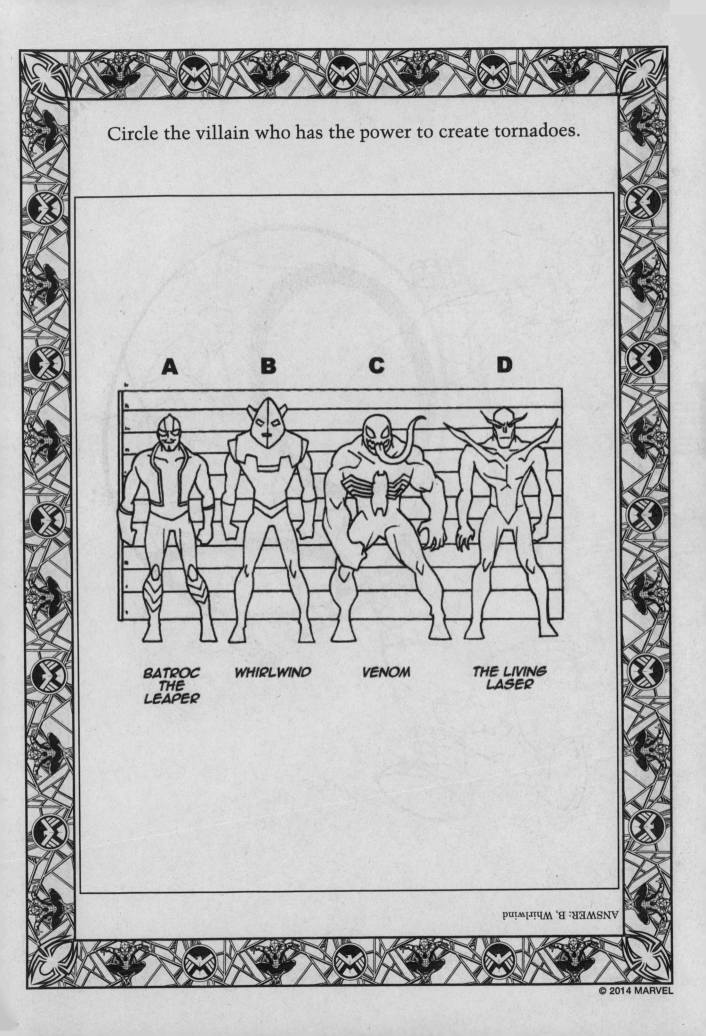

A   B   C   D

BATROC THE LEAPER   WHIRLWIND   VENOM   THE LIVING LASER

ANSWER: B, Whirlwind

Part of the story is missing! Fill in the missing comic panel.

© 2014 MARVEL

Taskmaster is hiding from our favorite web-slinger in one of the castle's secret passages. Complete the maze to help Spidey find Taskmaster.

Connect the dots to see why the Taskmaster
isn't attacking Spider-Man.